Joseph
the
Dreamer

and other Bible Stories

Retold by Vic Parker

Miles
Kelly

First published in 2011 by Miles Kelly Publishing Ltd
Harding's Barn, Bardfield End Green, Thaxted, Essex, CM6 3PX, UK

This edition printed in 2011

2 4 6 8 10 9 7 5 3

EDITORIAL DIRECTOR *Belinda Gallagher*
ART DIRECTOR *Jo Cowan*
EDITOR *Carly Blake*
DESIGNERS *Michelle Cannatella, Joe Jones*
JUNIOR DESIGNER *Kayleigh Allen*
COVER DESIGNER *Joe Jones*
CONSULTANT *Janet Dyson*
PRODUCTION MANAGER *Elizabeth Collins*
REPROGRAPHICS *Stephan Davis, Ian Paulyn*

ISBN 978-1-84810-395-5

Printed in China

British Library Cataloguing-in-Publication Data
A catalogue record for this book is available from the British Library

ACKNOWLEDGEMENTS
The publishers would like to thank the following artists
who have contributed to this book:

The Bright Agency Katriona Chapman, Dan Crisp,
Giuliano Ferri (cover), Mélanie Florian

Advocate Art Andy Catling, Alida Massari

*The publishers would like to thank Robert Willoughby and
the London School of Theology for their help in compiling this book.*

Made with paper from a sustainable forest

www.mileskelly.net   info@mileskelly.net

www.factsforprojects.com
Self-publish your
children's book

buddingpress.co.uk

Contents

A Tale of Twin Brothers

Isaac's mother, Sarah, lived to be one hundred and twenty-seven years old, while his father, Abraham, lived to one hundred and seventy-five. By the time they both died, Isaac had married a girl called Rebecca, from Abraham's old town of Haran. Isaac inherited his father's farming business and stayed in Canaan, following

God's will just as Abraham had done.

Like Isaac's father and mother, he and Rebecca had to wait a long time before God sent them children – twenty years. It was worth the wait, for when Rebecca finally found herself expecting a baby it was not one, but two – twins! A short time before they were born, God told Rebecca, "You are having two sons, who will lead two peoples. One boy will be stronger than the other and the older one will serve the younger one."

At the birth, a very strange thing happened. The second baby came out holding the first one's heel, as though he wanted to pull his older brother back and overtake. Isaac and Rebecca called the elder boy Esau, because the name means

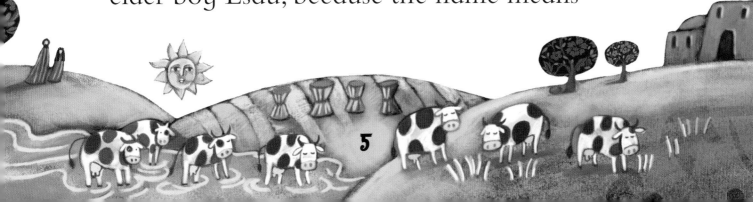

'hairy' and Esau was dark and had lots of hair. They named their younger, fairer son Jacob, which means 'someone who wants to seize somebody else's place'.

Time passed and the twins grew very different in personality as well as looks. Jacob was quiet and thoughtful. He loved spending time at home with his mother in the kitchen, and they became very close. However, Esau was strong and brave. He loved roaming around outside and he became an excellent hunter. Esau was his father's favourite son.

Whenever Jacob saw his father and

brother together, talking and laughing in easy companionship, he couldn't help but wish that he was loved best by Isaac instead. To make matters worse, because Esau had been born before Jacob, the law said that Esau was to be given all of their father's wealth when he died. This was called his birthright. Jacob knew that he was cleverer than Esau and better suited to running his father's business. He couldn't stand to think that it was Esau's birthright to take it over eventually.

One day, Jacob was in the kitchen cooking a delicious bean stew when Esau arrived back from a hunt. "Ooooh, what's that? I'm STARVING!" he exclaimed, bending over the cooking pot and breathing in the aroma. "Can I have some now?"

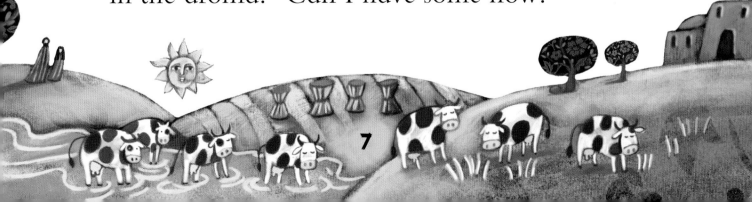

he begged.

Jacob's eyes glinted with a sudden idea. "I'll give you some stew," he replied, "if you promise to give me all your rights as the firstborn son."

"Done!" agreed Esau. All he could think about was his rumbling stomach, burning with hunger. "If I don't get anything to eat within the next five minutes I'll fall over and die anyway, so what use would my birthright be then?" he joked.

But Jacob was quite serious. "Say you

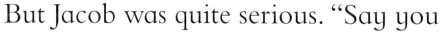

solemnly swear," he insisted.

"I solemnly swear," promised Esau. "Now come on, give me that stew!"

Jacob ladled some stew into a bowl and gave Esau some soft, baked bread, and both twins sat back, highly pleased.

Twenty years passed and Isaac was an old, blind man who knew he didn't have long to live. One of Isaac's last wishes was for Esau to go hunting for meat for his favourite meal. Afterwards, Isaac was going to give his eldest son the blessing that officially gave him his birthright. Esau set off with his bow and arrows at once.

But Rebecca had overheard. All at once, a plan came to her to trick her husband into giving her favourite son Jacob the blessing instead! First, she quickly cooked

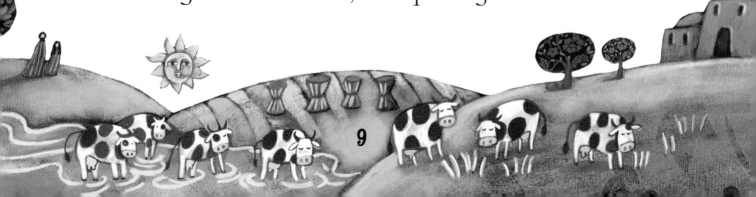

the meal her husband had asked for. Then she hurriedly dressed Jacob in Esau's clothes so he would smell like his brother, and wrapped goatskin round his arms and neck so he would feel hairy like his brother too.

"But- But- " protested Jacob.

"I'll take the blame," Rebecca reassured her son, and sent him in with the food to see his father.

The trick worked perfectly. Isaac was at first suspicious because his tasty dinner had arrived so quickly, but Jacob said that God had helped him in his hunting. Jacob copied Esau's voice and, of course, he smelled and felt like his brother too. Isaac was fooled into thinking that Jacob was Esau, and gave him the all-important birthright blessing.

When Esau arrived back from the hunt

and went to his father, they both quickly realized they had been tricked. How they wept with frustration and regret. But it was too late, the old man could not take back his blessing.

Later, in private, Esau began to feel angry. "I'll wait until father dies," he swore to himself, "but no longer than that. Then I shall have my revenge on Jacob."

Genesis chapters 25 to 28

Jacob's Dream

Jacob had won his twin brother Esau's birthright, but his joy soon melted into shame and regret. His old, blind father was so bitterly disappointed that he could hardly talk to Jacob, and Esau couldn't stand the sight of him either. It was only because Esau didn't want to upset his father even further that he hadn't already had a fight with his smaller, weaker twin brother. Only Jacob's mother still loved him – and now he was about to lose her too. Rebecca was so worried about what Esau would do to her favourite son once Isaac died, that she told Jacob he had no choice but to leave. "You must go far away, well out of Esau's reach," Rebecca urged. "Hurry to my brother, your Uncle Laban, in the city of Haran. You'll be safe there. We'll just have to hope that your brother cools down and forgives you, so you can come back."

So Jacob left his home and his family in disgrace, with no one for company and no possessions for comfort. He set off for Haran through the desert, wondering why he had done what he had done. At the end of the first lonely day's travelling, Jacob came across a rocky, sheltered spot where he could camp for the night. Weary and miserable, Jacob found a flattish, smooth stone that would have to do as a pillow and laid down to try to get some rest.

Alone in the desert, hungry, cold and worried about wild animals, Jacob did not sleep well. He tossed and turned for hours, and when he did eventually fall asleep he had a very strange dream.

Jacob dreamt that a blinding light suddenly burst from the dark night sky. He shielded his eyes and blinked until he got used to the glare and could open them properly. Then Jacob saw that the light shone in a steady, sloping beam down to the ground. People in bright, shimmering clothes were gliding up and down. With a shock, Jacob realized that he was looking at a staircase from Heaven to Earth and that the people were angels. Suddenly he felt God Himself standing beside him. "Yes, I am the Lord," said God. "And as I promised your grandfather Abraham and your father Isaac, I am going to give the land on which you are lying to you and your family. You will have as many descendants as there are specks of dust on the ground.

Now remember, you will never be alone. I will always be with you. I will look after you, and wherever you go, I will make sure that one day you return safely back home."

Then the staircase and the angels faded away and the voice was gone. Jacob woke up, lying stiff and cold on his own in the desert. But he knew God had been there and was watching over him.

Genesis chapters 27, 28

Jacob Makes Amends

Jacob reached Haran and went to work on his Uncle Laban's farm. He vowed to work for his uncle for fourteen years, and he married Laban's daughters Rachel and Leah.

Jacob was a very skilled farmer. With him in charge, his Uncle Laban's flocks and herds grew several times bigger and the sheep, cattle and goats were fatter and finer than ever. Jacob stayed longer than the fourteen years he had promised, and built up stocks of animals for himself. Eventually he became even wealthier than his uncle.

Finally Jacob decided that enough was enough, he wanted to return home. He told his wives and they ordered the servants to pack everything up and prepare the animals. They all set off in a long train across the countryside.

As Jacob drew closer to Canaan, he became more and more worried. After all, when he left, his brother Esau had been determined to kill him! Jacob sent messengers galloping ahead, to tell Esau that he was coming and that he wanted to make amends. But he was worried to see his messengers returning so soon. "Sir," they panted, "your brother is heading this way with a force of four hundred men!"

"Then Esau must have made up his mind to attack me," Jacob told himself in deep dismay. He ordered his herders to count out two hundred and twenty goats, two hundred and twenty sheep, thirty camels and their young, forty cows, ten bulls and thirty donkeys. "Keep all the animals separate," Jacob instructed the herders. "Drive every group forward an hour apart and when you each reach Esau, tell him that the animals are a present from me." Jacob thought that perhaps by the time he sees Esau, he may have forgiven him.

That evening Jacob camped on his own. He knew it might be his last night. As darkness drew in, he lay awake thinking.

Suddenly, from nowhere, a man jumped on Jacob and began to attack him. Stunned, Jacob fought for his life, but the stranger didn't give in. They wrestled for hours, until finally – CRACK! Jacob collapsed in agony as one of the stranger's blows put his hip out of joint.

"I am the Lord," the stranger announced, and Jacob was stunned to realize that it was God Himself. "You have done well," God continued. "You have won your struggles with others and now I say you have won your struggle with me too.

I want you to change your name. From now on, everyone should call you Israel."

The sun rose and God was gone, and Jacob hobbled away to rejoin his family.

It wasn't long before Esau and his four hundred men arrived in a cloud of dust. Jacob told his family to stay well back and limped forward all alone to face his brother. Esau jumped off his horse and ran forwards, and Jacob sank to his knees before his brother, bowing low. But Esau hurried to help him up, throwing his arms around Jacob, kissing him, and both the brothers began to weep.

"Welcome, my long-lost brother," Esau sobbed. "Welcome to you and your family."

Jacob was overjoyed to be home at last.

Genesis chapters 30 to 33

Joseph the Dreamer

Jacob was one of the wealthiest men in Canaan. He had vast herds of cattle, sheep, goats, camels and donkeys, and he owned many tents, filled with possessions. However the thing he held most dear was Joseph, his eleventh son, the first of two sons by Jacob's true love, Rachel. The couple had waited for many years before God sent them a child. So long that Jacob had ten sons by three other wives by then. So Joseph was very special.

Unfortunately, Jacob made it obvious that Joseph was his favourite. He sometimes kept Joseph at home with him while his other sons went into the fields on farming duties. Of course this made Jacob's other sons resentful of their brother. Even more so when Joseph turned seventeen. Jacob had a coat made for him.

It was a beautiful, long coat with big sleeves, richly sewn with many different colours. It drove Jacob's other sons wild with jealousy.

The situation went from bad to worse when Joseph began to have strange dreams.

"Guess what?" he asked his brothers one morning. "Last night, I dreamt that we were in the fields at harvest time tying the wheat into sheaves, when my sheaf stood up straight. Then your sheaves gathered around it and bowed to mine!"

"Who do you think you are?" spat one of the brothers.

"Do you see yourself as better than us?" growled another.

"Do you think you're going to be a king and rule over us?" scowled a third.

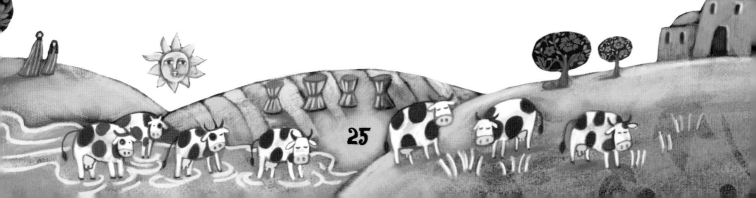

A little while later, Joseph had another odd dream and again made the mistake of telling his brothers about it.

"I dreamt last night that I saw the sun, the moon and eleven stars all bowing down to me." The brothers knew that Joseph meant that their father, mother and the eleven of them were like his servants. How furious they were!

One day, when Jacob had kept Joseph at home with him and sent his other sons out to work, he decided to send Joseph to check on them. Out in the hot fields, the tired, thirsty brothers saw him coming, fresh from home, all dressed up in his fancy coat and they had a terrible idea.

"Here comes the dreamer!" one of them laughed. "I wish we could get rid of him."

"Well, this is our chance," another noticed.

"There's no one around, it's the perfect opportunity!" a third brother agreed.

"Let's kill him and throw the body into that pit over there," another brother urged.

"We could tell our father that he was attacked by wild animals!" one lad suggested.

"Stop it!" cried the eldest brother, Reuben, horrified. "We can't kill Joseph! Do you really want his blood on your hands?" he pointed out. "If you must, throw him into that old, dry well over there and leave him – but don't murder him!" (Little did the brothers know that once they'd all gone home, Reuben intended to sneak off back to the well and rescue Joseph).

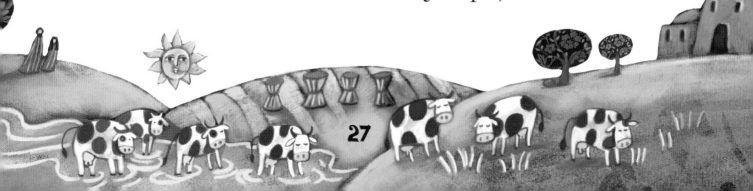

And that's what the brothers did. They fell on Joseph, ripping off his special coat, and then lowered him into the dried-up well, taking away the rope.

Pleased with themselves, the brothers ignored Joseph's cries for help, and sat down to eat – all except Reuben. He didn't feel like joining them. He stomped off on his own to see to the animals in the furthest pastures.

While Reuben was gone, a camel train of spice traders came passing by on

their way to Egypt. One of the brothers, Judah, had another awful idea. "Reuben was right. We shouldn't harm Joseph – he is our flesh and blood, after all," he announced, with a glint in his eye. "I have a better plan – we'll sell him instead. I'm sure the traders will pay a good price for a slave."

By the time Reuben returned, Judah and the brothers had accepted twenty pieces of silver from the traders and Joseph was gone.

"What have you done?" Reuben cried. "Shame on you, Judah. Shame on you all! Now what are you going to tell Father?"

In desperation, the brothers came up with a final part to their wicked plan. They killed a young goat, dipped Joseph's torn coat in its blood and took it home to show

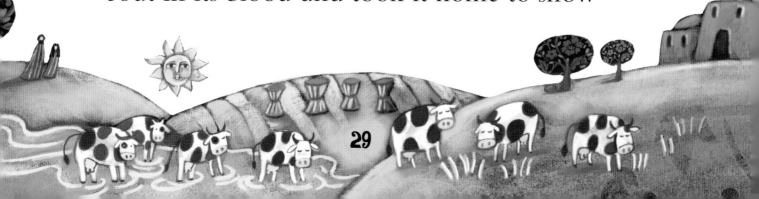

their father. "Joseph was killed and eaten by wild animals," they explained to Jacob.

The old man collapsed in sorrow, weeping and mourning for his beloved Joseph. "I will grieve for my son until the day I die," he sobbed.

Genesis chapter 37

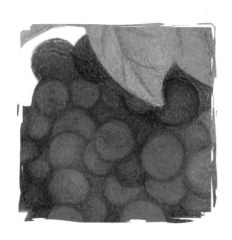

A Slave in Egypt

Sold by his family, marched by strangers all the way to a foreign land, and then traded in the market place as a slave – Joseph was exhausted and terrified. Yet his strong character must have shone through because the man who bought Joseph trusted him to work in his house, not in his fields or as a labourer. The man was very important and wealthy. His name was Potiphar and he was captain of the soldiers who guarded Pharaoh, the king of Egypt. God stayed with Joseph all the time and cheered him up, helping him do his duties well. Potiphar was so pleased that he kept promoting Joseph. After a while, Joseph was running Potiphar's whole household.

Now Joseph was not only hard-working and trustworthy, he was also quite handsome. So much so that Potiphar's wife fell in love with him. Each day, she seized every opportunity behind her husband's back to flirt with Joseph, trying to tempt him into having an affair. Joseph was loyal to Potiphar and kept turning her down. But Potiphar's wife was determined to get what she wanted.

One day, she lay in wait for Joseph and grabbed him by his cloak. Joseph had to wriggle out of it in order to escape her clutches and run off!

Then the scorned woman saw a way to get her own back. She put on a show of being deeply upset and accused Joseph of having forced his way into her bedroom. She said that when she screamed out, he had ran away, leaving only his cloak behind.

Of course, Potiphar was furious. He had

Joseph flung into prison.

Joseph could have wept and wailed. He could have despaired and died, but God stayed with him and lifted his spirits.

The jailer was fond of the reliable, capable young man and began giving him special jobs. Soon, he put Joseph in charge of all the other prisoners.

Two of the prisoners in Joseph's care were Pharaoh's butler and baker. One morning, Joseph found them looking anxious because they had both had strange dreams that they couldn't understand.

"Tell me about them," Joseph urged. "Maybe God will explain to me what they're about."

"I dreamt I saw a vine on which three branches of grapes grew," said the butler.

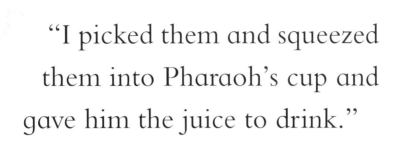

"I picked them and squeezed them into Pharaoh's cup and gave him the juice to drink."

Joseph felt sure he knew what the dream meant, thanks to God. "In three days' time Pharaoh is going to pardon you and give you your job back," he explained.

The butler was delighted. "Oh thank you! Thank you so much!" he cried.

"My friend," Joseph said, "just promise me that when you're released, you won't forget about me. Please tell Pharaoh about me and beg him to release me, for I don't deserve to be in here!"

"Well, what about my dream?" asked the

baker excitedly. "I dreamt I was carrying three baskets of white bread on my head, and the birds were eating the bread out of the top basket."

Joseph's face fell as the meaning came to him. "I hate to tell you this," he said sadly, "but in three days' time, Pharaoh is going to hang you."

The dreams came true. In three days' time the baker was put to death, while the butler was released and set back to work for Pharaoh. He was so joyful that any thoughts of Joseph went out of his head. Joseph remained in prison, quite forgotten.

Genesis chapters 39, 40

The Ruler of Egypt

One morning, there was a commotion in the royal palace of Egypt. Pharaoh had awoken deeply troubled. He had had two strange dreams which he was sure meant something – but he had no idea what.

In the first dream, Pharaoh had been standing by the River Nile. Seven fat cows

37

came out of the waters and started grazing. Then came seven more cows – but this time all skin and bones. The thin cows ate up the fat cows, but they didn't look any healthier. In the second dream, Pharaoh saw seven ears of corn growing on a stalk. They ripened and turned golden. Then he noticed seven small, shrivelled ears of corn sprouting and they swallowed up the big, full ears.

Pharaoh had summoned all his wise men, but none of them had an explanation.

Suddenly, the butler remembered Joseph. Two years had passed and he wasn't even sure if Joseph was still alive. But now he told Pharaoh all about the amazing young Israelite man locked in the dungeon.

Pharaoh sent for him at once. Joseph was hauled out of prison and brought into the magnificent courtroom of the great King of Egypt. Then Pharaoh described his dreams and Joseph felt God give him the interpretation.

"Both dreams mean the same," Joseph announced to the anxiously waiting king. "For the next seven years, Egypt will have excellent harvests. But during the following seven years the crops will fail and there will be a terrible famine. Here's what God says to do. Hire a minister with officials under

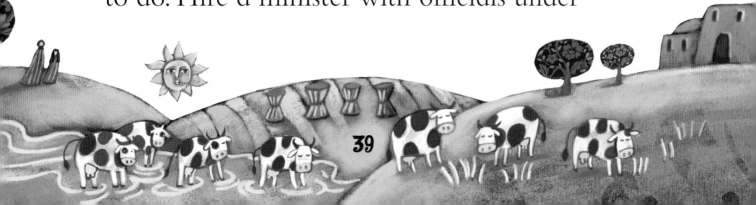

him to take charge of your kingdom. For the next seven years, they should collect one-fifth of all the grain that is grown and store it away in warehouses. During the seven years of famine, you can share out the grain so your people don't starve."

"Really?" said Pharaoh. "Is that what your God thinks?" He thought for a while and everyone in the courtroom held their breath to see whether the king was pleased.

Pharaoh descended from his gleaming throne and approached Joseph. He took a huge gold ring off his finger and gave it to the former prisoner. "You will be the minister," he ordered. "I can't think of anyone better. You start straight away."

Genesis chapter 41